Scene Changes

SCENE CHANGES

OSBERT LANCASTER

Illustrated by the Author

LONDON
JOHN MURRAY, ALBEMARLE STREET, W1

Filmset by
Richard Clay (The Chaucer Press), Ltd., Bungay, Suffolk
and printed in Great Britain by
Fletcher & Son Ltd., Norwich

0 7195 3567 0

Author's Note

The drawings in the first part of this book formed a self-contained section of a most admirable, if gloomy, exhibition entitled 'The Destruction of the Country House' organised by Dr. Roy Strong in the Victoria and Albert Museum to demonstrate what was happening to what we have come, rather belatedly, to call our architectural heritage. This section, called 'Great Houses of Fiction Revisited', recounts the changes that 'progress' has made to the houses conceived by novelists—such as Mansfield Park by Jane Austen, Chesney Wold by Charles Dickens, Gatherum Castle by Anthony Trollope, Blandings Castle by P. G. Wodehouse—when the owners or their heirs were no longer able to maintain them on the scale for which their authors designed them or to which they were accustomed.

Those in the second part, which have no didactic or cautionary purpose whatsoever, were conceived as a purely personal contribution to the general wave of largely congratulatory self-examination which tourism provokes.

The last part consists of purely personal reactions to a selection of what the Germans in their pithy way call *sehenswürdigkeiten*. That the text is in verse is due to a desperate and, from the author's point of view, entirely successful, attempt to relieve the tedium of caption writing. Whether they render the task of caption reading any lighter it is not for him to say.

O.L. 1978

CONTENTS

Great Houses of Fiction Revisited

*   *   *

The Englishman's Profound Horror

*   *   *

Afternoons with Baedeker

GREAT HOUSES
OF FICTION
REVISITED

The original drawings were exhibited
in the Victoria and Albert Museum
exhibition 'The Destruction of the
Country House'

MANSFIELD PARK

Mansfield Park School for Girls was first established in the old home of the Bertrams shortly before the 1914 war. The Principal Miss (afterwards Dame) Prism, was a woman of exceptional ability (and considerably greater energy, than her elder sister, Mrs. Chasuble) and under her direction the school soon achieved an enviable reputation. Between the wars the intake rapidly expanded and it soon became necessary to extend the accommodation provided by Wyatt's original house. The stables were transformed into a Jane Austen gymnasium and a converted conservatory, which had hitherto been used for divine worship, was replaced by the beautiful Memorial Chapel designed by Sir Edward Maufe. After the war a new dormitory wing, the work of Sir Basil Spence, was added to the west of the central block balancing the stables on the east. While the proportions of Wyatt's façade were carefully respected, no attempt was made to achieve any unconvincing pastiche and the result was immediately recognised as a forthright and welcome expression of twentieth-century ideals in a contemporary idiom. Finally, last year saw the opening of the new science block, the work of a distinguished Danish architect which, carefully sited just off the main axis of the old façade, provides a discreet and agreeable contrast to the pilastered splendours of a bygone era.

BRENTHAM

'And yet it would be difficult to find a fairer scene than Brentham offered, especially in the lustrous effulgence of a glorious English summer. It was an Italian palace of freestone; vast, ornate, and in scrupulous condition; its spacious and graceful chambers filled with treasures of art, and rising itself from statued and stately terraces. At their foot spread a gardened domain of considerable extent, bright with flowers, dim with coverts of rare shrubs, and musical with fountains.'

BENJAMIN DISRAELI *Lothair*.

Right up to the outbreak of the last war this splendid mansion, designed by Giacomo Leoni with later additions by Adam, was maintained by its noble proprietors in very much the same state as it was in Disraeli's day. Late in 1939, however, it was requisitioned by the War Office who have retained possession ever since. What exactly goes on in the house itself and the 600-acre park which surrounds it has, despite repeated enquiries by the C.P.R.E., the Historic Buildings Board and innumerable local preservation societies, never been revealed. Some say that it is an atomic warfare research centre; others that such activities as take place, which insofar as they are known to the locals would appear to be slight, are, in fact, largely connected with army catering. Whatever the truth, the military authorities continue stoutly to maintain that their retention of Brentham is absolutely essential on grounds of National Security.

CROTCHET CASTLE

'In one of those beautiful vallies, through which the Thames (not yet polluted by the tide, the scouring of cities, or even the minor defilement of the sandy streams of Surrey), rolls a clear flood through flowery meadows, under the shade of old beech woods, and the smooth mossy greensward of the chalk hills (which pour into it their tributary rivulets, as pure and pellucid as the fountain of Bandusiu, or the wells of Scamander, by which the wives and daughters of the Trojans washed their splendid garments in the days of peace, before the coming of the Greeks); in one of those beautiful vallies, on a bold round-surfaced lawn, spotted with juniper, that opened itself in the bosom of an old wood, which rose with a steep, but not precipitous ascent, from the river to the summit of the hill, stood the castellated villa of a retired citizen.'

THOMAS LOVE PEACOCK

Ebenezer Mac Crotchet Esq., the original owner of this charming villa, an early work of the celebrated Mr. Nash, was but the first of a long line of stockbroking occupiers. When, some ten years ago, the last of his successors abandoned his Thames-side residence for a villa in the Algarve, the whole estate was purchased by a neighbouring firm of gravel pit developers. The 'bold round-surfaced lawn' and the old wood soon vanished, but, much to the new owners' annoyance, the house had been made the subject of a preservation order. However, while the law forbade its destruction it did not require its maintenance, and total neglect combined with flooding is likely to insure the final disappearance of this pathetic folly in a matter of months.

CHESNEY WOLD

On the death, at a very advanced age, of Sir Lester Dedlock, Bt., Chesney Wold passed to the eldest son of the Hon. Bob Stables who had inherited all his father's sporting tastes and now found himself in a position unreservedly to gratify them. Unfortunately neither he nor his successors ever acquired any grasp of estate management and were forced, ever more rapidly, to rely on timber as their main source of revenue, so that by the time of the outbreak of the Second World War the surrounding woods, to which in Dickens' day the place owed so much of its melancholy charm, had all but vanished. Those that remained were disposed of by a timber speculator who acquired the estate in 1946; the great avenue, however, survived for some years longer only to fall at last to the bulldozers of the Ministry of Transport at the time of the construction of the M21. It is, however, much to the Ministry's credit that it was found possible to retain the splendid entrance gates on their original axis. The house itself, a late Tudor building heavily remodelled in the mid-seventeenth century, still stands and now houses the records of the Rural District Council. Curiously enough the haunting of the long terrace still continues and the sound of the menacing footsteps regularly heralds an imminent pile-up on the M21, invariably attended by a heavy loss of life.

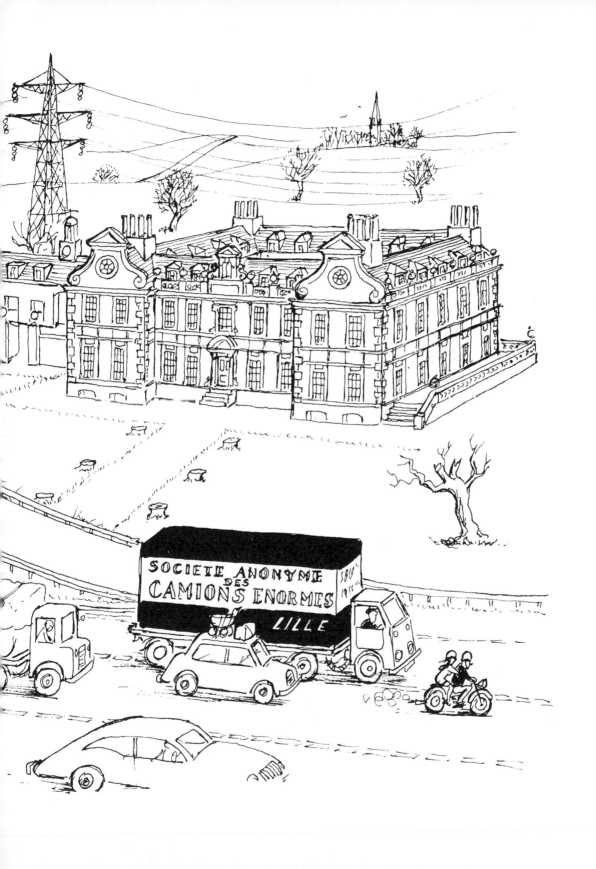

LOCKSLEY HALL

' 'Tis the place, and all around it, as of old, the curlews call,
  Dreary gleams about the moorland flying over Locksley Hall.'

ALFRED LORD TENNYSON

Even during the poet's lifetime The Hall, in common with many
another building on our eastern coasts, was threatened by the
erosion of the sea. Early in the present century the family abandoned their Lincolnshire estates and the house, together with about
a thousand acres of moorland, was sold to a local farmer from
whom it passed, after a lifetime of incessant and barely profitable
toil, to a son. The latter, less persistent than his father, took the first
opportunity of letting the immediate surroundings of the house as a
caravan site. The house itself was for a time used for storage pur-
poses but when during the last war a large packet of 'ghastly dew'
fell alongside, it was finally abandoned to its fate. However, the
recent construction of the Locksley Hall Marina has most fortun-
ately served to halt the sea's advance, and made it possible to
convert the stable wing into holiday flats and it is hoped that the
picturesque ruins of the main block may survive for many years yet
to delight future generations of holiday makers and other visitors to
this sternly beautiful coast.

'Howsoever these things be, a long farewell to Locksley Hall!
Now for me the woods may wither, now for me the roof-tree fall'

GATHERUM CASTLE

Thanks to the energy and enterprise of the present Duke of Omnium this splendid pile, generally regarded as Salvin's masterpiece, is carefully maintained much as it was in Trollope's day. All the principal rooms including the Long Gallery with its magnificent range of Palliser portraits and Glencora's boudoir, carefully restored to its original state, are open to the public throughout the year (Adults 50p, children 25p). To the natural beauty of the surroundings have been added a variety of specialised attractions—water skiing on the lake, roaming bison and Ethiopian lions, a scale model of the Stockton–Darlington railway complete with a working reproduction of Stephenson's rocket often driven by the Duke himself in period costume. During the summer the park is regularly the scene of well-organised pop festivals and student 'happenings' and in the vast basin of the Tritons' fountain topless bathing is not only permitted but encouraged. It is not surprising, therefore, that Gatherum should have become one of the most popular of all our ancient seats and that each year sees a spectacular rise in the takings.

BLANDINGS CASTLE

When, quite recently, economic circumstances forced Lord Emsworth to dispose of his ancestral home, it was a source of considerable satisfaction to him that he was able, having successfully resisted his sister's pressure to sell it to a prominent Chicago soft-drinks tycoon, to hand over Blandings to the Ministry of Agriculture for the establishment of the National Pig Board's Breeding Research Centre. In recognition of his own great contribution to this branch of knowledge, the Ministry gladly granted him for his lifetime a rent-free leasehold of the lodge-keeper's cottage at the end of the West Drive whence he can keep a disapproving eye on the efforts of the experts, not yet crowned with any marked success, to produce a rival to the Empress. Much of the interior of the house has been converted to the uses of bureaucracy but the ancient fabric remains largely untouched and the grounds are open to the public on certain days, after due application has been made in writing. Last summer much of its former glory was restored when the castle was for a time the scene of the 25th Annual Conference of the International Bacon-curers Association. The ancient walls were floodlit, pigs were roasted on the lawn, and there was a display of morris-dancing, particularly appreciated by the foreign members.

THE ENGLISHMAN'S PROFOUND HORROR

These cartoons were drawn for the
Coronation issue of The Ambassador

The Englishman's profound horror
of any sartorial ostentation . . .

fostered by education,

reinforced by tradition,

every stage of his career,

and common to all classes

of society

in every part

naturally makes it very difficult for him to comprehend
the foreigner's passion for fancy dress.

AFTERNOONS WITH BAEDEKER

The first eight Afternoons were included in the collection of drawings entitled
Façades and Faces

ITALIAN AFTERNOON

IN yonder marble hero's shade
Aunt Drusilla used to sit
With her memories of the Slade
And her water-colour kit.

There, E. V. Lucas lay, well-thumbed, beside her,
Buckling a little in the foreign sun,
While round that dim *Risorgimento* rider
[Claiming some long-forgotten vict'ry won]
The circling pigeons' flight grew ever wider,
Fainter the echoes of the midday gun.

Across the square a monsignore
Late for his siesta goes:
The prison scene from *Trovatore*
Dies on a dozen radios.

EIREANN AFTERNOON

THE distant Seychelles are not so remote
Nor Ctesiphon as ultimately dead
As this damp square round which tired echoes float
Of something brilliant that George Moore once said:
Where, still, in pitch-pine snugs pale poets quote
Verses rejected by the Bodley Head.
For in this drained aquarium no breeze
Deposits pollen from more fertile shores
Or kills the smell of long unopened drawers
That clings for ever to these dripping trees.
Where Bloom once wandered, gross and ill-at-ease,
Twice-pensioned heroes of forgotten wars
With misplaced confidence demand applause
Shouting stale slogans on the Liffey quays.

BAVARIAN AFTERNOON

ERNST Maria Ludwig Karl
Kurfürst, Herzog, Fürst und Graf,
Built this rococo Taj Mahal
In order he might have the laugh
Over the Prince of Dachshundstal
Whose schloss was smaller by a half.
Time passed; the Duke was buried 'mongst his peers.
The dust grew thicker on the chandeliers,
And tourists, who preferred the Gothic style,
Greeted this gay façade with pious jeers.
But for this long-dead Duke's presumptuous pile
Were yet reserved triumphant final years
Bathed in the sunshine of a Sitwell's smile,
Before collapsing with a faint 'sieg heil'.

AEGEAN AFTERNOON

BENEATH the kite-encumbered sky
There reigns a silence in the heat
Which natives here would classify
As tense, unbroken and complete.
An Asia Minor refugee
Wails a nostalgic Turkish song.
The priest at the Asomatoi
Is beating on a wooden gong
And fishermen far out at sea
Are dynamiting all day long.
In the spongeshop Vassilias
Gives a deep, responsive snore
As the streamer from Piraeus,
Hooting loudly, nears the shore.

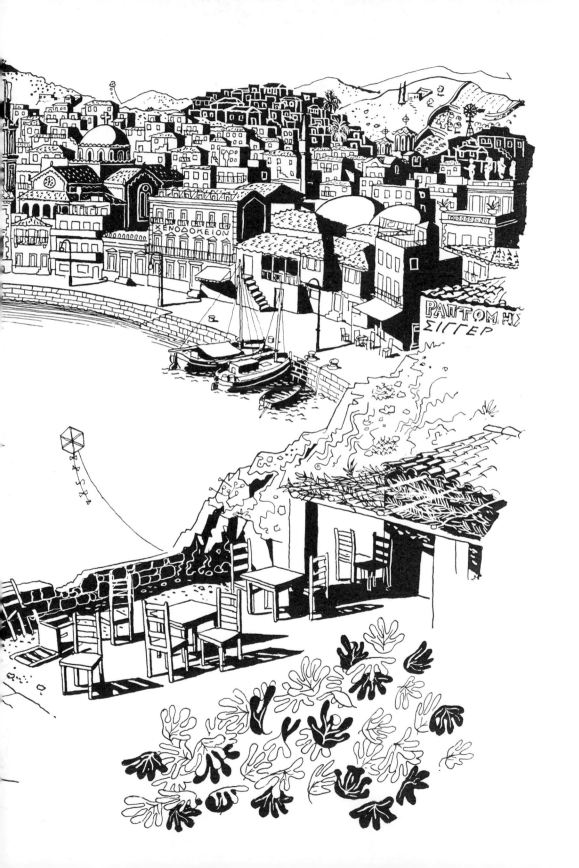

ENGLISH AFTERNOON

IN 1910 a royal princess
Contracted measles here;
Last spring a pregnant stewardess
Was found beneath the pier;
Her throat, according to the Press,
Was slit from ear to ear.

In all the years that passed between
These two distressing dates
Our only tragedy has been
The raising of the rates,
Though once a flying-bomb was seen
Far out across the straits.

Heard on this coast, the music of the spheres
Would sound like something from *The Gondoliers*.

FRENCH AFTERNOON

I SHALL not linger in that draughty square
Attracted by the art-nouveau hotel
Nor ring in vain the concierge's bell
And then, engulfed by a profound despair
That finds its echo in the passing trains,
Sit drinking in the café, wondering why,
Maddened by love, a butcher at Versailles
On Tuesday evening made to jump his brains.
Nor shall I visit the Flamboyant church,
Three stars in Michelin, yet by some strange fluke
Left unrestored by Viollet-le-Duc,
To carry out some long-desired research.
Too well I know the power to get one down
Exerted by this grey and shuttered town.

LEVANTINE AFTERNOON

THE lofty column, moss bedeckt,
Where once a sainted stylite sat
Displays a summons to elect
An unattractive Democrat.

Above the shrine of Artemis
The English church, by G. E. Street,
Proclaims, with Gothic emphasis,
A faith which triumphs over heat.

Here past and present, side by side,
In perfect amity are met;
The call to prayer is amplified
In every mosque and minaret.

And placid Turks distribute Marshall Aid
Playing backgammon in a plane-tree's shade.

MANHATTAN AFTERNOON

HERE those of us who really understand
Feel that the past is very close at hand.
In that old brownstone mansion 'cross the way,
Copied from one that she had seen by chance
When on her honeymoon in Paris, France,
Mrs. Van Dryssel gave her great soirées;
And in the chic apartment house next door
J. Rittenhaus the Second lived—and jumped,
The morning after General Motors slumped,
Down from a love-nest on the thirtieth floor.
Tread softly then, for on this holy ground
You'd hear the 'twenties cry from every stone
And Bye-Bye Blackbird on the saxophone
If only History were wired for sound.

79

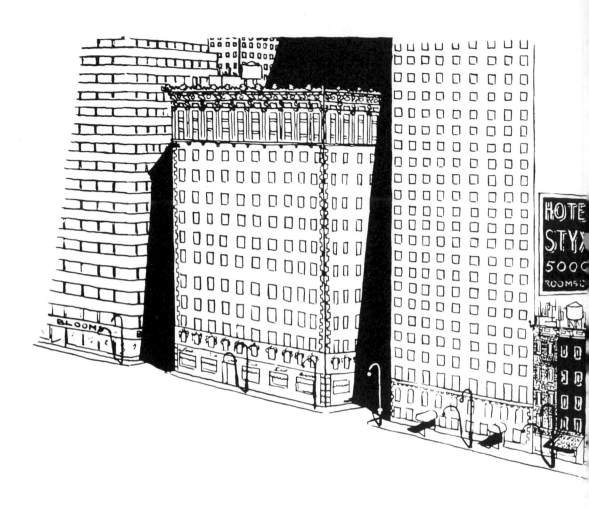

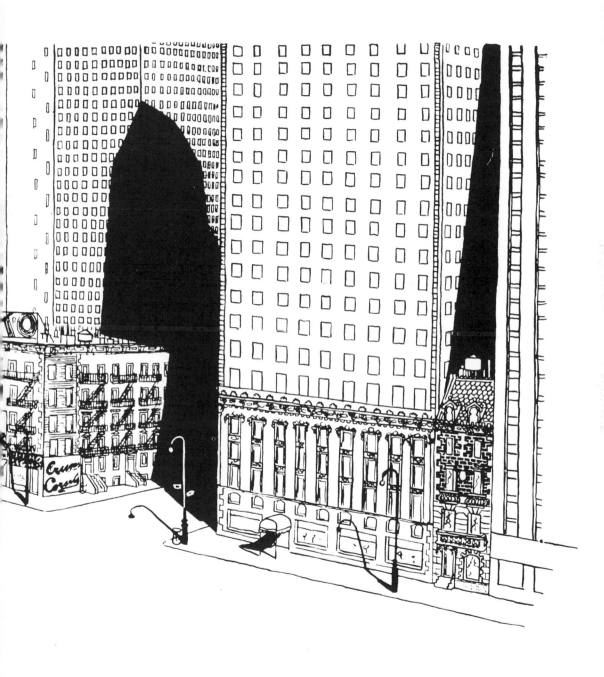

CITY OF LONDON AFTERNOON

FUR-CLAD, the Master and the Wardens go
    To worship at St. Aethelfryth's Within
And hear their chaplain speak of guilt and sin.
(The posters tell us 'STERLING HITS NEW LOW').
There sculpted Aldermen and marble Mayors
And long dead Sheriffs etched on Flemish Glass,
Armigerous but sternly middle-class,
Approve their presence and sustain their prayers.
From every steeple floats a chime
Reminding us it's opening time.
Bank messengers in faded pink
Foregather for an early drink
While pigeons coo and copulate
From Temple Bar to Billingsgate.

EGYPTIAN AFTERNOON

THE call to prayer is on the air,
The pale-faced tourists stop and stare
At mysteries they cannot share.
The kites are circling overhead
But Beys and Mamelukes are fled
And Russell Pasha, too, is dead.

Long since that beautiful P.A.,
The toast of the Mo' Ali Club,
Has gone on her triumphant way,
Administered her final snub.

Gone the Romans, gone the Greeks,
Gone the soldiers of the Queen,
But the water-wheel still squeaks
A greeting to the fellaheen.